Omba Bolomba

*For childhood friends Donald May, Teresa Jones, Jacqueline
Brinkworth and Wendy Smith (wherever they are now)*
GB

*For Janette, Rosalie, Jackie, Sue,
and Mary Sansom*
CB

Previous publications by Gerard Benson

Name Game (Oyster Publications 1971)

Gorgon (a poem in eight parts) (Paranomasia Press 1984)

The Magnificent Callisto (Blackie Poetry Originals 1992/ Puffin 1993)

In Wordsworth's Chair (Flambard Press, in association with the
    Wordsworth Trust, 1995)

Evidence of Elephants (Viking 1995) (nominated for the Carnegie
    Medal 1996)

Bradford & Beyond (Flambard Press 1997)

Hlep! (fifteen poems with woodcuts by Ros Cuthbert) (Yellow Fox
    Press 2001)

To Catch An Elephant (Smith/Doorstop Books 2002, illustrated by
    Cathy Benson)

Co-editor: *Poems on the Underground* Anthologies (ten editions); *Love
    Poems on the Underground*; *London Poems on the Underground*;
    Comic Poems on the Underground; *New Poems on the Underground*
Editor: *This Poem Doesn't Rhyme* (Viking 1990/Puffin 1992) (winner
    of the Signal Poetry Award 1991); *Does W Trouble You?* (Viking
    1994/Puffin 1995)

Some of the poems in this book have been published in *The Apple
Raid* (Macmillan), *Bonkers for Conkers* (Macmillan), *Frogs In Clogs*
(Macmillan), *Funny Poems* (Scholastic), *The Spectator*, *The Upside
Down Frown* (Wayland), *Wizard Poems* (Macmillan), *The Works 4*
(Macmillan).

Omba Bolomba

Poems by Gerard Benson

Illustrated by Cathy Benson

Smith/Doorstop Books

Published 2005 by
Smith/Doorstop Books
The Poetry Business
The Studio
Byram Arcade
Westgate
Huddersfield HD1 1ND

ISBN 1-902382-70-6

A CIP catalogue record for this book is available from the British Library.

Typeset at The Poetry Business
Printed by Charlesworth & Co. Ltd., Huddersfield
Cover design by Cathy Benson

Distributed by Central Books Ltd., 99 Wallis Road, London E9 5LN

The Poetry Business gratefully acknowledges the help of Arts Council England and Kirklees Metropolitan Council.

CONTENTS

Ducks

Ducks are cleverer than people think.
They lead secret lives that you wouldn't guess at.
At night they come out of the ponds
And go round the shops taking notes

And photographing things in the windows.

They write ponderous articles about quack doctors.
They complain to the council about the tin cans,

And often put stickers on parked cars.

And they can swim without getting wet.

Shaking the Branches

I'm shaking our walnut tree,
standing in its fork,
and I can see for miles.

A farmer is ploughing
with one piebald horse.
And the crows are flying.

It's not a school day.
The sun, low on the horizon,
is bright in my eyes.

My fingers are stained
with walnut juice;
my bare knees are cold.

There are apples in the barrel
and tomatoes on the sill;
and on the range, a juicy stew.

The swallows have gone
and smoke is curling
from the tall twisty chimneys.

My parents are a hundred miles away
in a bombed city.
Churchill is on the news,

and I am standing in the fork
of a walnut tree
shaking the branches.

Lock the Dairy Door

Old Fox comes trotting over the hill
  Down from Caistor Tor,
On through the woods by the water-mill.
  Lock the dairy door.

He's an orange flame in the early light
  As he sneaks between the trees,
With his tail down low and his sharp eyes bright
  He sniffs the morning breeze.

Near the farm he drops his speed.
  Head to the ground he goes.
There are hungry cubs in the den to feed.
  He twitches his clever nose.

The proud cock struts by the chicken run,
  He sees the fox come by
And calls out loud to the morning sun,
  Raises his head to the sky.

Sisters! Sisters! Get out of here!
  Go and roost in the old grain store.
A prowling fox is lurking near.
  Lock the dairy door!

Lock the dairy door!
   A fox is lurking near.
Sisters, get out of here.
   Lock the dairy door!

Old fox goes trotting past the farm,
   Turns north toward his lair.
Now no chicken will come to harm,
   But you rabbits – beware!

In Britain most roosters call 'cock-a-doodle-doo'.
In France it's 'cocorico', in Germany 'kikerikee'.
But in some parts of the country listen carefully
And you'll hear the cock call, 'Lock the dairy door!'

Old Bryn

Bryn my uncle's donkey
Lives in the blue barn.
His garden is the paddock.
   He doesn't do any harm.

He's usually pretty patient.
He'll stand by the top gate,
And till you come with his bucket
    He'll wait and wait.

His ears are long and mobile,
His hoofs small and neat,
His coat is warm and rough,
    His muzzle soft and wet.

When I bring him an apple
He'll raise his head,
And trot to where I am
    With a delicate tread.

We take him to market;
He carries our gear.
He rarely complains.
    What does he fear?

A child in a tantrum,
A man with a stick;
But Bryn can bite
    And Bryn can kick.

Do You Like Butter?

She said, 'Do you like butter?'
And held the little flower
Close under my chin
To make a golden reflection.
And, yes. I love it – butter
Smeared thick on new bread.
And I remember making butter
In the yard at Grady's Farm,
Stirring at the milk with a long pole
That fitted through a hole
In the lid of the wooden churn –
And turning it and turning and turning.

The mixture got heavier and heavier,
And harder and harder to move,
And my arms ached; I longed to stop.
But you had to keep on going
Till the butter was ready,
Slopping about in the churn
With a hollow slap slap,
And that milky, baby-like smell.

And I remember Dilys and Nancy,
The girls in the dairy
Patting it into shape
With little wooden bats;

And I remember the cows at milking time
Plodding up from the river
Swinging their udders
Through grass and yellow buttercups.

Thinking

A small chair
In a garden shed
And a small boy
Sitting alone.

Sitting alone
In a striped T-shirt
(The one that made him
Look like a zebra).

Sitting with a book
On his knees;
It's open on his knees
But he's not reading it.

Perfectly at peace,
He's looking at the sky
Through the shed window
Looking at sailing clouds.

Sitting in his small
Basket-work chair
And thinking, I suppose.
Yes. Thinking. Just thinking.

Rainbow Riddle

I held a rainbow in my hand today –
A perfect circle covered with black words
Which held another which I could not see;
It sang to me as sweetly as the birds,

    A song, as round and round it whirled,
    Then stopped. Have you guessed what I held?

Boxes

1

Shopping bags hang from the handle
Of this box on wheels;
There's a sleeping passenger
Under the retractable roof.
A lady is pushing it along.

2

The lid slides back, the layers swivel;
Your name is printed on the top.
Side by side are the long thin tubes,
Black, green, red, blue, sharp-ended
Gold-printed, with a little blob of rubber.

3

It looks like a London bus
But it isn't going anywhere.
It's made of tin and it's airtight.
But who are the passengers? Are they Crackers?
Or Jammy Dodgers? No. They're Ginger Nuts.

4

A shaped box of quivering silence
Rigged with four stretched strings
And sprinkled with a little white dust
Rests inside another box,
Custom-built, curvy and velvet-lined.

5

A broad-shouldered box
With flowers on top;
They carried it out
And into a long black car.
It'll never come back in.

Fire Riddle

I saw a great fire,
Huge, fierce, but so distant
That it seemed no more
Than the twinkle in an eye.

From where I stood
It looked icy cold,
Although I knew
It was a blazing furnace.

Soon more fires than I could count
Thronged around it;
Making silvery patterns
That I learnt to recognise.

But at the first fire,
As soon as I saw it
I rhymed out loud.
And made a wish.

THE LIGHTHOUSE

This is the light
that shines so bright
to warn the shipping
through the night.

This is the beam which sends a stream
of precious light, of golden light
to guide the sailors through the night.

This is the tower
of brick and stone
that stands so tall
and all alone.
It's painted white
and holds the light
that sends a beam
into the night
to warn the sailors
far out at sea
of dangerous rocks
that out of sight
can wreck shipping
in the dark night.

This is the island rocky and small
that holds the light that stands so tall
to send the beams of precious light
that guide the sailors in the night.

This is the sea
that laps around and sometimes has a gentle face
and sometimes lashes at the base
and sometimes makes a murmuring sound
at other times it roars all night and splashes to an awful height
against the lonely island's light.

Omba Bolomba

Omba omba babalo pom,
Ambi pongalong, ding ding brom.
O pori, do pori slib slob slom,
Omba palomba babaloli dom.
    Pin pinni lili pot?
        Pin pinni plee!
    Bin binni pipi lot?
        Wa la pee!
Omba golomba babalo pom,
Ambika zambika zim zim zom!

Not That I'm Superstitious

I'm bending to pick a four-leaf clover,
When a big dog comes and knocks me over.

So I cross my fingers and spit three times
And all of a sudden the town clock chimes.

And believe me or believe me not,
That mad clock strikes thirteen – that's what.

But am I scared? No not in the least
For one thing I was facing east.

And late last night I wished on the moon.
And I always carry a wooden spoon.

So unless I spill some salt tonight,
I and my friends will be all right.

No, Honestly

The Invisible Man came to tea.
He came and sat right on my knee.
   He ate all the ham
   And most of the jam
And everyone blamed it on me.

How Delightful to Know Mr Benson

*H*ow delightful to know Mr Benson
Everyone wants to know him –
So witty and charming and handsome
(Though some think he's ugly and dim).

His quips never verge on the personal,
Though sometimes he puns people's names.
He's a lifelong supporter of Arsenal
But it's years since he went to their games.

He moved up to Yorkshire from Highbury
To devote extra time to his rhymes,
And he lives in a sort of a library,
And tends a small garden, sometimes.

He hasn't been made Poet Laureate.
His face hasn't been in *Hello!*
(Two facts that he's not all that sorry at)
But, (ah!) he's delightful to know.

A Pod of Common Dolphins

No maths book
   ever showed
      the curves
         their bodies make
        as they tunnel
       through the waves
    like living waves
  themselves,
   their powerful small
     bodies streamlined –
      chocolate brown
       and creamy white.
      They travel in groups
    and play, it seems,
  with our pleasure ship
  as we cross the bay,
    diving under the prow,
      or leaping in the wake,
        riding the bow-wave.
     Arched and sociable,
   elegant and beautiful,
  their blow-holes snorting,
   they muscle
     through the water,
       rolling, one over another.

Legends have them
        ferrying the souls
            of the dead,
        and rescuing boys
    who've swum beyond their depth.
Watching them now
    it's easy to believe
        that even while they play
            round our hurrying ship
                in this broad open water,
                they are speaking,
        perhaps to us
    in a language more ancient
than the earth,
    more universal
        than the sea.

People

They point down
from the low-flying plane.

Look! they say.
People!

Parrot

*P*arrot flames on his branch;
his beak is a battle axe.

His encircled eye
pierces what it sees.

He screams like a soprano;
moves among the leaves like a rock climber.

He dazzles the forest canopy
with primary colours. A celebration.

Hidden Child: A Polish Christmas, 1940

Dark-haired little Naomi
Stared in amazement.
Under an indoor tree
(A tree indoors?)
Were little parcels in a row,
And from the branches,
In twists of coloured paper,
Nuts and raisins grew.

Beyond the front door,
Soldiers patrolled;
She could hear their boots.
She could hear singing too:
A Christmas song, a carol –
Silent Night, Holy Night,
Soldiers somewhere singing together,
Sweet harmony. Sweet, sweet.

Her new sisters and parents
Smiled in the candle-light.
Her first Christmas present –
A wooden doll in a cotton dress.
Outside, in the Christmas darkness,
Herod's soldiers, searching for Jews
Trod the cold pavements
In massive boots.

The Two Strange Sisters

The Good Luck Goddess
And the One who brings Bad Luck
Go with us wherever we walk.
                Yuan Hung-Tao

I've two invisible sisters,
Who walk with me wherever I go.
    One brings sunshine,
    One brings snow.

    One brings happiness,
    One brings sorrow.
    Wherever I go
    They're sure to follow.

    One on my left,
    One on my right,
    They stay beside me
    Both day and night.

    One brings joy
    And one brings woe.
    They walk beside me
    Wherever I go.

My two invisible sisters
Are always beside me,
And in their different ways
They guide me.

One More Day
(Snapshot haiku)

Sunrise. Alarm clock.
The dark sharp smell of hot toast.
Dress in a hurry.

Kids sauntering past
The usual gang at the gate.
The bell calls us in.

Measuring hands, now.
And I'm looking forward to
Literacy hour,

(Well, sometimes we read
A story or poem that's
Quite interesting).

Big boys and small boys.
Girls chat in groups by the fence.
Thud of a football.

Pizza and baked beans,
With long yellow half-warmed chips
(We call them bendies).

Huge cardboard cut-out:
I'm painting these monster eyes,
Bloodshot and glaring.

Bullies on the bus.
Then biscuits, sofa, TV.
Supper afterwards.

Bed-time, pyjamas
Quick wash, tingle of toothpaste.
Stare from the window.

When the sky's blackest
And there's not even a moon,
The stars are brightest.

School For Wizards And Witches

2nd Witch: Fillet of a fenny snake
In the cauldron boil and bake.
Macbeth, *Act 4, Sc.1*

So today, children, we will learn to make
   Fillet of a fenny snake.
Now now, Caspar, none of your moans and groans;
   Get on with it and remove those bones.

No, Mervyn, not a *funny* snake. Fenny!
   It comes from a fen, Kenny.
That's wicked! really disgusting, Matilda.
   No dear. I don't know what killed her.

Matilda, show the others your fillet.
   No, Simon. We can't grill it.
It's for our spell. Caspar, for badness' sake
   Give Sybil back her fenny snake.

Give it back, child. You've got one of your own.
   And leave those poisoned entrails alone.
No, Sybil. Slice lengthwise; by candlelight.
   Get Merle to show you. Yes, that's right.

Lobo. Take that poisonous toad off your shoulder.
   Put it in your coursework folder.
I've told you ninety-nine times. You know the rule:
   No pets. No pets allowed in school.

Careful, Nostrodamus, don't spill that slime!
　　Where's my hourglass? Is that the time!?
Everything away! Whooshky-cadabra! That's right!
　　Or we won't be home before midnight.

You've all been really evil today.
　　So tomorrow I'll give you an hour's play
While I bake the snake. But look at that sky!
　　Badnight, wizlets. I must fly.

Wet Playtime

(Dave's Version)

Mr Finn
Lets us stay in;
Mrs Grout
Makes us go out.

Mr Finn

Makes us stay in;
Mrs Grout
Lets us go out.

The Night Creatures

*T*hey live behind the cupboard,
And they hide under the bed.
 And they're thin …
So thin that if I touched them
I'd feel nothing; but my head
 Would spin.

They wait till I'm almost asleep,
With my head under the clothes
    Then they creep
On silent invisible toes
    To where I lie,
Hardly daring to breathe.
And they gather round
    And they sigh,
    (A creepy sound)
And they touch my pillow
And talk about me in whispers.
    And underneath
The duvet I lie quite still, oh
Ever so still. But my heart
    Is like a drum.

And they guard the light switch.
    (That's the worst part.)
And I call out – and if Mum
Or Dad come in, or even a baby-sitter,
    They steal away.

But if no-one comes
    They stay.

The Guide

'How strange to meet you on this moor ...
But you are lost. Here, take my hand.'
The hand was colder than a knife;
I held it though, for dear, dear life,
        For dear, dear life,
And on we walked through that weird land,
Myself behind, my guide before.

I followed on behind my guide.
Her clothes gave off an eerie glow.
'Who are you? *What* are you?' I said
'I'm what I am.' She turned her head,
        She turned her head.
'Ask me no questions, for I know
Nothing, not even how I died.'

She never spoke another word;
And so we walked all through the night,
Past twisted tree and lumpen stone
Till the sun rose, and all alone,
        And all alone,
I found myself, bathed in the light
And sung to by the dawning bird.

And I was safe, as heaven knows.
But who my strange companion was,
What wistful ghost had held my hand,
To guide me through that unknown land,
    That nightmare land,
I never, ever learned, because
She vanished as the bright sun rose.

The Two Wizards

The Wizard of the North,
He came to visit me.
He blew in as a snow-storm;
So I became a tree.

Then he became a Polar ship
And I became the keel
So he became a walrus,
And I a barking seal.

Then he became an icicle,
So I became a flame.
Then he became a howling wind
And I became the same.

And together we blew,
Together we blew,
Till nobody knew
Which was I and which was he
And neither did we,
Neither did we.

History Lesson

1

*T*here was nothing, then dinosaurs, then
There were mammals and finally men,
Who ruled for a while
In belligerent style,
And then there was nothing again.

2

*F*rom the start there've been wars without cease:
Just think of the Trojans and Greece,
Or think about ours
Or the Great Superpowers',
But remember: they all fought for Peace.

2 ZIKENI

ZIKEN 1

ninizik ninizik kiki nini zek zek,
kenikiki kenikiki, ikni kek.
   ekni ikni izni kizni
    ekni ikni kinikini nek.
ninizek nikinek nek zek kek.

ZIKEN 2

eziii   eziii
ezi ne ne niii
eziii kneziii
ezine zine ziii.
   zin
   zin
knenkiii knenkeee
eziii   eziii
ezi ne ke niii

A Firm Parent

*N*o.
No.
Definitely not.
No ... really. I mean it.
No.
No. Really. It wouldn't be right.
No. I'm not kidding.
I've told you before. No.
No. Don't try my patience.
I've said ... No.
That's No. N – O. No,
Two consecutive letters of the alphabet. 'N' and 'O'.
No. Not now. Not tomorrow. Not ever.
You can go on as long as you like. It's still No.
Do I make myself clear?
No.
No no no no NO!
*

Oh all right then,
but just once. OK?

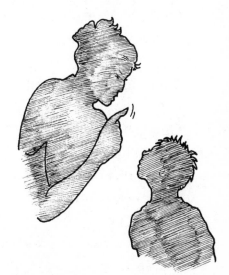

If I Hadn't Been a Writer

If I hadn't been a writer,
　　I might have been a vet,
Or then again I might ha'
　　Played the drums in a Quintet,
Been a plumber in the summer
　　When the weather's nice and hot,
And a printer in the winter
　　To be indoors when it's not.

I might have been a dancer
　　(No, not a ballerina
But a tapdance fancy-pantser),
　　I have been a window-cleaner;
Or I could have been a waiter
　　Or at least a washer-upper.
Or the bloke behind the counter
　　Who serves you with your cuppa.

A postman, a bricklayer,
　　Or a boxer or a ref,
Or a pub piano-player,
　　Or a butcher or a chef.
Or a barber or hair-dresser,
　　A caretaker or teacher
Or even a professor,
　　Or, at a pinch, a preacher.

But I might be something quiet,
    A librarian perhaps,
An adviser about diet,
    An expert on old maps;
Or something with adventures,
    A stuntman (that's exciting!)
And catch bullets in my dentures …
    No! I think I'll stick to writing.

Good Luck!
or
Sound Advice from the Poet

(who spilt salt onto a black cat
under a ladder one Friday,
and lived to tell the tale).

Never bake bread on a Sunday
If the wind is in the West,
Or stand on your head on a Monday
If you're wearing a long-sleeved vest.

If you meet with a ginger-bearded man
You should pull your ears and sing,
Or say this rhyme as fast as you can,
Or dance the Highland Fling.

Never wear skates in swimming pools,
Quack when you pass a duck.
If you keep to all these simple rules,
You'll always have good luck.
        Good luck!

Not Really a Riddle

Marvellous mathematician,
Mistress of the spiral curve;
She makes her own house.

Carrying her eyes in front,
She steps bravely into the world
With her whorled home on her back.

She cares nothing for silver.
Whenever she goes walking
She leaves a little behind her.

Now she sits on the school wall
Just above the lion painting.
Some call her wall-fish, some hodmandod.

Speed is not her priority.
Once at dawn I watched her
For half an hour as the sun rose!

While she climbed to the top
Of a long flat leaf of grass,
Taking her time. Taking her time.

Tiddlywinks

What have you got in that trailer?

Two tons of tiddlywinks.

Two tons of tiddlywinks?

Yes. Two tons of tiddlywinks and a tiddly tailor.

Two tons of tiddly winks and a tiddly tailor?

Yes. Two tons of tiddlywinks, a tiddly tailor and a tiny toddler.

Two tons of tiddlywinks …?

Yes. Turkish tiddlywinks.

Two tons of tiddlywinks from Turkey …?

Yes. Tried and tested Turkish tiddlywinks.

Two tons of tried and tested Turkish tiddlywinks, a tiddly tailor and a tiny toddler?

Yes. A tiny toddler with a tatty Teddy.

A tatty Teddy?

Yes. Two tons of tried and tested …

Aaaargh! No-o-o-o! Stop! I can't take it. What are they doing?

Playing I Spy with My Little Eye Something Beginning with T.

A tiddly tailor and a tiny toddler with a tatty
Teddy and two tons of tried and tested Turkish
tiddlywinks, playing I Spy with My Little Eye
Something Beginning with T?

Yes. A tiddly tailor and a tiny toddler with a tatty
Teddy and two tons of ...

Where are you taking them to?
Torrington? Taunton? Tilbury? Tullyfergus?

Southend-on-Sea. Toodle-oo.

Dan Malone & His Mobile Phone

th grtest joy v Dn Malone
wz txtng on iz mbl fone
hed txt on trains or at the pool
hed sit n txt al day at schl
IT or Inglsh Mths or Gym
it made no dffrnce to him
hed txt awA thn 4 a jke
he startd txting unknwn fk
hooz numbuz he hd slyly got
wth inslts n I dont no wot
sch as Hlo ol smlly feet
n thngs id rthr not rpt
o alrt thn if U insist
Hi monkEbum Ur round th twst

1 day he txtd by mstake
th Yr 9 bully Evl Jake
calling im donkybrane. Wots more
ths Jake wz in th Rm nex dor
n wen E got the txt saw red
n jst about went off iz hed
so wen th buzza went E ran
to ware E new Ed find poor Dan
n tried to grb im by th throat
bt Dan escped leaving iz coat

n made off lke a strk of litning
(th idea of a fite wz fritning)
Jke chsd im 3 X round the yrd
n wen E cort im thmpd im hrd
then wen the pr were separ8ed
thr mbl fnz wer confisc8ed
(wich didnt teach em not 2 QuarrL)
bt tales lk this shd hav a moral
th MORAL is obA th rul
dont Uz yr mbl fne in skl
[:-((-:]

The Alien's Shopping List

*F*ace Paint (for looking almost human),
   Bubble Gum. Baseball Cap.
Xigloglometer (about time I had a new one),
   Astrolabe. Star Map.
Earth Boots (in case I have to walk),
   Tezzophonic Stun-Gun (small),
Babble Machine – with Enhanced Squawk,
   Tickle-twizzler, Hanky, Football.
Quinquivalator (preferably Martian)
   Chocolate, Expanding Sandwich Box,
Joke book, Riddle-solver, Cybernetic Cushion,
   G-Booster, assorted Star-Clocks.

Bunions

There was an old man with a bunion,
Who said, 'This new cure is a funny 'un.
    You plunges your foot
    In a Wellington boot*,
Which you've carefully smeared with an onion.

'So I follows the rules to the letter.
I promise, I didn't forget a
    Bit of the cure.
    Of that I'm quite sure,
But it didn't make anything better.'#

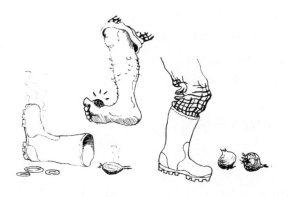

Footnotes (get it?)
* He came from Invergordon, where these words rhyme.
# Well, it wouldn't. He put the onion on the outside of the boot instead
  of the inside. What did he expect?

Overheard On Safari

Look!
There's a flock of elephants
Galumphing across the horizon.

Herd of elephants.

Of course I've heard of elephants.
I was just telling you,
I saw a flock of them over there.

Herd!

Not from here you can't.
Unless you've got sharper ears than mine.
You can't hear them from here.
Even a big flock like that.

It's a HERD of elephants.

Yes, I know. Of course it is.
I've got eyes in my head.
I was just pointing them out to you.

The Earwig Football Song

Earwig Oh,

Earwig Oh,

Earwig Oh!

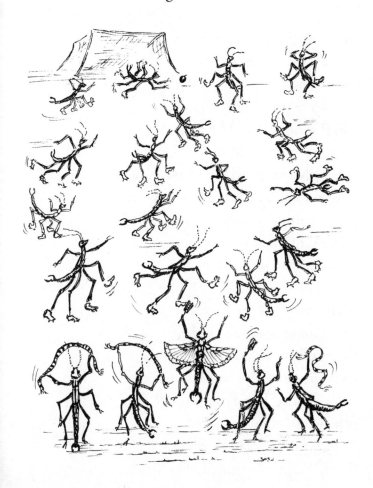

sdrawkcaB gniviL

*E*rus ton m'I … No. I'll translate:
I'm not sure when it began.
Perhaps it was when a stroke of lightning
Yad eno hit the bedroom mirror.

*

I remember watching my pen
Skilfully extracting the words
From a sheet of paper,
Starting at the bottom right
And flowing upward line by line
Till the page was clean.
Gradually I emptied the whole book,
So messy and mucked up at first,
Now beautifully clean.
I took it to the shop.
They paid me some money.
I put it on a shelf
With others like it.
They looked so lovely in their row,
So organised, so very special.
I was proud of my work.
But what had they done wrong?
Why would they be taken
Away from here and slowly
Slowly but surely turned into trees?

I pitied those lovely books.
Outside it was niaring at first.
I walked away quite quickly,
Keeping a sharp eye on where I'd been
And watched the water
Lifting from the puddles
And felt my coat as it became lighter,
More comfortable and at last quite dry.
On my way home I pulled a few letters
From the big red post box,
Ready to open them and unwrite.

*

And here I am again with my pen
At the bottom of a full sheet of paper.
What's that written at the top?
'SDRAWKCAB GNIVIL'. What does it mean?
I'll get there. Don't worry.

Index of first lines

*G*erard **Benson** was born and brought up in London. He was evacuated for a while during the Second World War – so he came to enjoy the country as well as the big city.

He has written poetry since he was a child but has earned his living in many ways, though not quite as many as he mentions on p.48. With two friends he runs the 'Poems on the Underground' scheme in London. For many years he toured, performing poetry and music with the famous Barrow Poets.

He lives in Yorkshire with his illustrator wife, Cathy, with whom nowadays he also does voluntary work for peace and justice. He sometimes visits schools, to work with children on their poetry.

He loves a good joke and quite likes bad ones.

*C*athy **Benson** was born in Bradford but she spent her childhood in a seaside town in Scotland.

She always drew. No writing pad, envelope or paper bag was safe from her, and when she ran out of paper she drew in the sand.

When she grew up she married, had three children, became a teacher, owned five cats, reared stray animals: woodmice, assorted birds, hedgehogs, beetles (yes! beetles), frogs, crayfish and even a duck.

She left teaching to do more writing and painting and to travel with her second husband, the poet Gerard Benson.

Her mind has travelled through the poems in this book and these are the pictures she saw.